This Buddy Book belongs to

_____

Table of Contents

Writing New Words 2

Writing in a Journal 56

My Writing Collection 88

Writing New Words

A
P
M
B
J
E

Each day you will learn more and more words. In this section of your Buddy Book, you can write the new words you learn and draw pictures to go with the words.

3

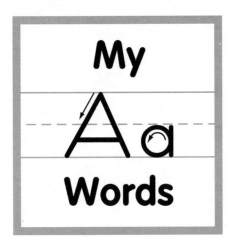

My **Aa** Words

4

My B b Words

A
B
C
D
E
F
G
H
I
J
K
L
M
N
O
P
Q
R
S
T
U
V
W
X
Y
Z

My

C c

Words

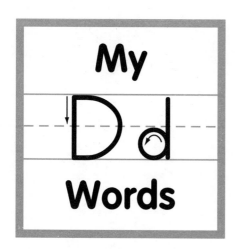

My **D d** Words

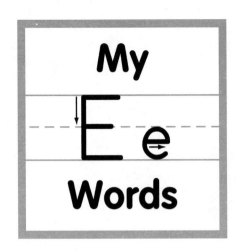

My **E e** Words

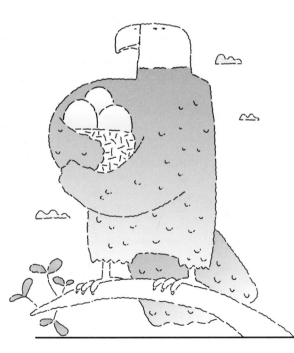

12

My

F f

Words

14

My **Gg** Words

16

My

H h

Words

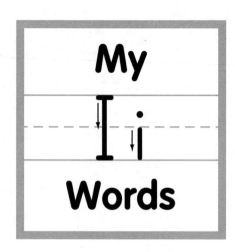

My
I i
Words

My J j Words

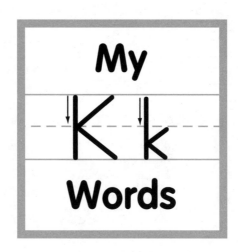

My **Kk** Words

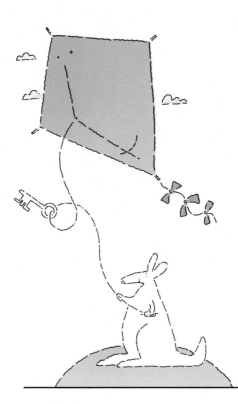

My Ll Words

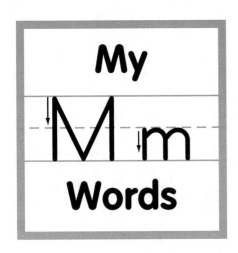

My **M m** Words

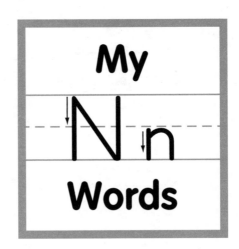

My **N n** Words

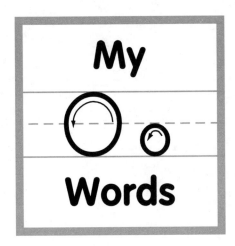

My

Words

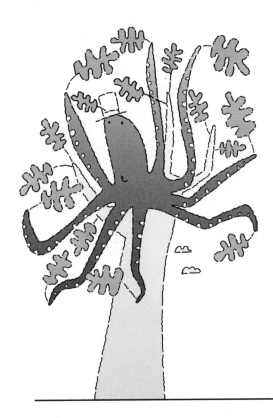

32

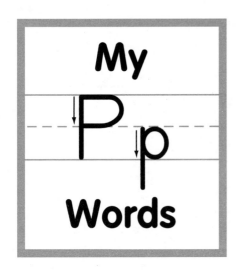

My

P p

Words

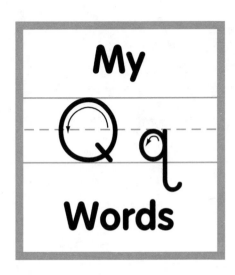

My Q q Words

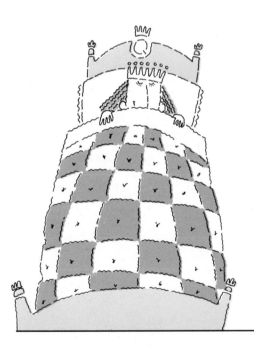

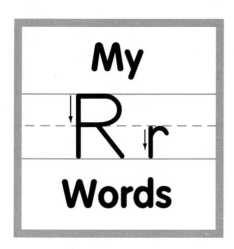

My **R r** Words

My

S s

Words

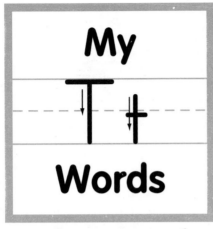

My **Tt** Words

My U u Words

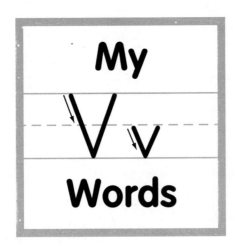

My

V v

Words

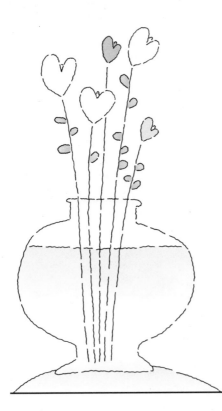

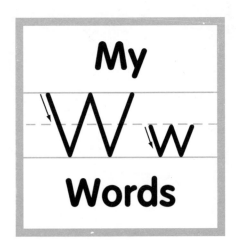

My **Ww** Words

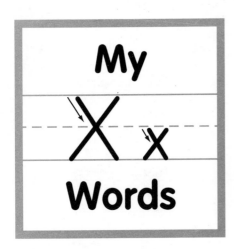

My
Xx
Words

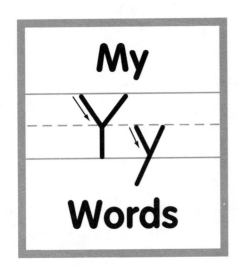

My Yy Words

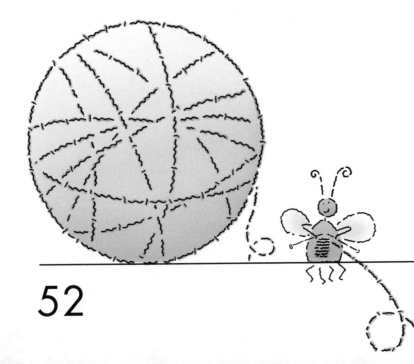

My Z z Words

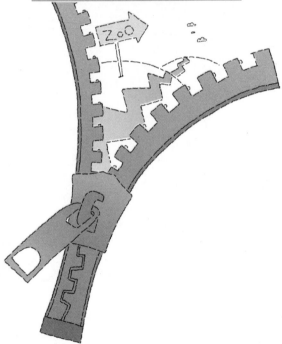

Writing in a Journal

A journal is a place to write about the things you do. The first time you write in your journal, your teacher may help you get started. Soon you will be able to write on your own. See pages 38-39 in *Write One* for ideas.

In this section you'll find plain pages, half-lined pages, and lined pages. You may fill these pages with pictures, writing, or both. You decide!

When you write in your journal, spell words the best way you can.

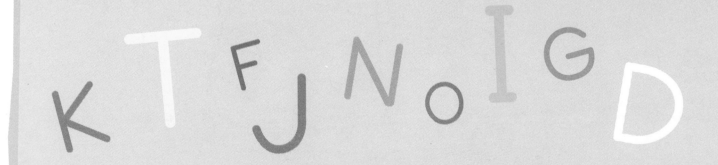

Date

Date

Date

Date

Date

Date

Date

Date

Date

Date _____

Date

70

Date _____

Date _____

Date _____

Date _____

74

Date

Date _____

76

Date _____

Date _____

78

Date

Date

Date

Date

Date

Date

84

Date

Date _____

86

Date

My Writing
Collection

Use this section of your Buddy Book to try all kinds of writing. You can write notes, lists, stories, letters, poems, and much more. It can become your own writing collection to read and to share with others.

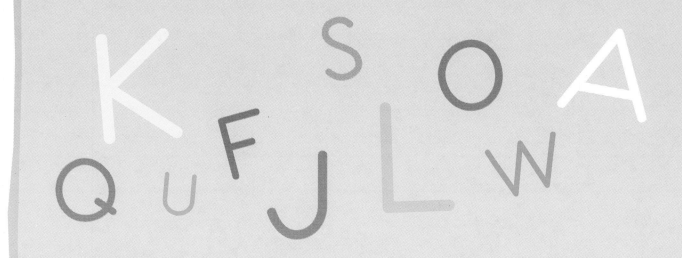

Writing Lists

Write your own lists on these pages.

Show
what you
know in
this list.

A List About _____
(your topic)

Have fun
writing
this list.

Special Words I Like to Say

Writing Friendly Notes

Write friendly notes on these pages. If you want to send a note, make a copy on your own paper.

A Note for Someone Special

A Thank-You Note

Writing Friendly Letters

Write a letter to someone, using the form below.

_____
Date

_____
Greeting

Message

_____
Closing

_____
Your name

94

Practice addressing an envelope.

_____
_____
_____

USA

_____

_____

_____

On envelopes, the U.S. Postal Service asks
you to use all capital letters and no punctuation.

Writing a Story About Me

Plan a story about a happy time you had.
Then write your story on the next page.

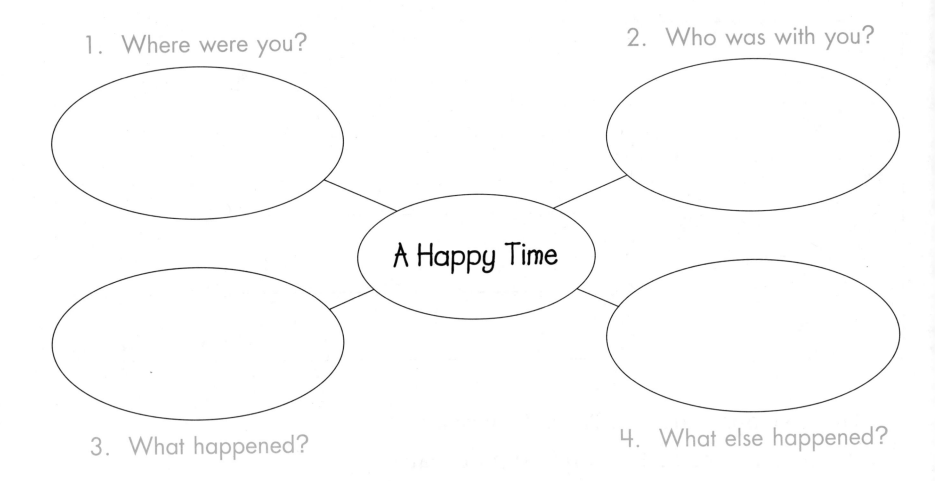

1. Where were you?

2. Who was with you?

A Happy Time

3. What happened?

4. What else happened?

A Happy Time

Writing About Others

Draw a picture about a person who is special
to you. Then write a story about the person.

Special person's name

A Special Person

Writing a Description

Draw a picture of a person, place, or thing.
Then write a description of your picture.

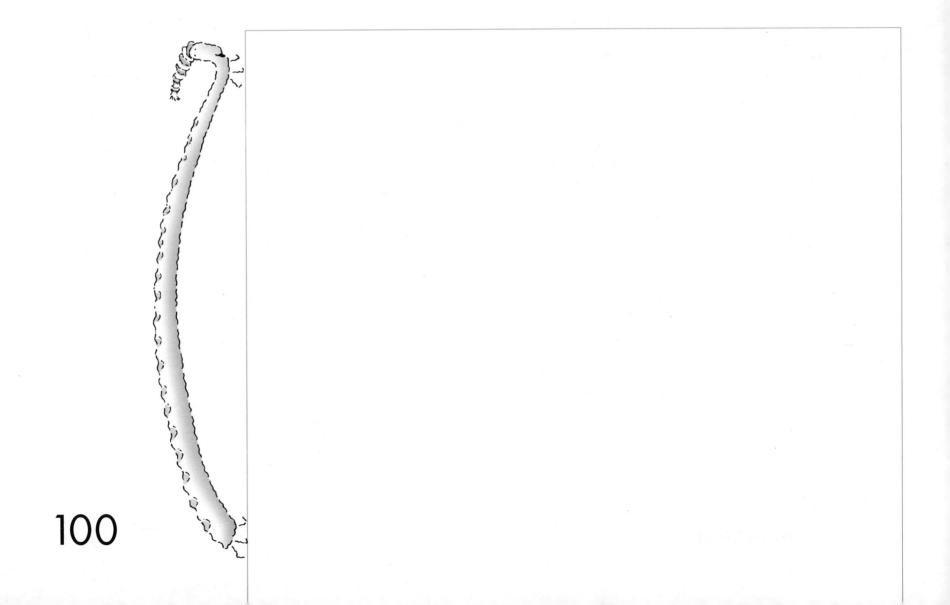

100

Use your senses to describe your picture.

Writing Directions

Choose something you know how to do.
Draw pictures of the steps.

1.	2.
3.	4.

Write down the steps for something you know how to do.
(Use the pictures on page 102 to help you.)

1.

2.

3.

4.

Writing Captions

Paste or draw pictures in these two spaces.
Write a caption for each of them.

Color this bulletin board. Write a caption about colors.

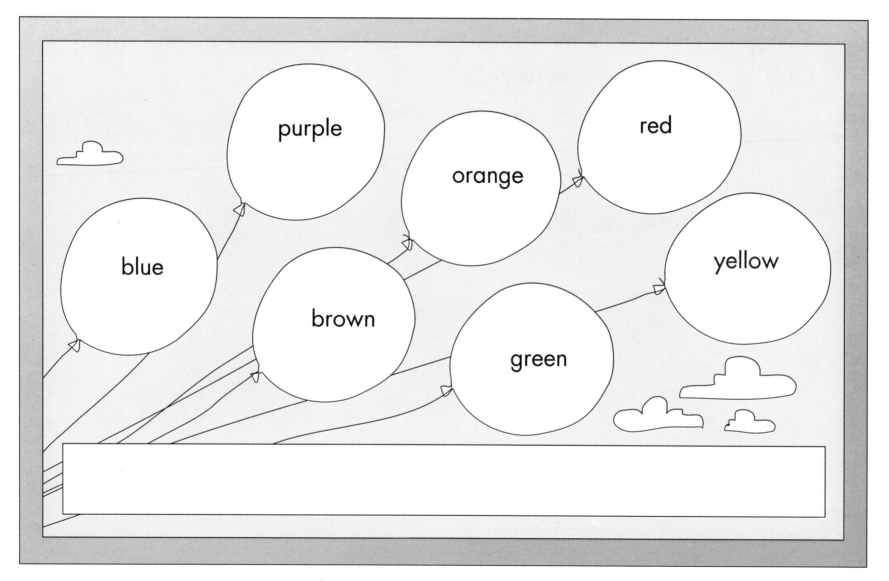

Writing a Story

Draw a picture about something happening to a person or an animal. Then write a story on the next page to go with your picture.

Be sure your story has a beginning, a middle, and an ending.

Writing Poems

Try writing three different kinds of poems on these pages.

Writing with a Pattern

Read the nursery rhyme on this page. (You probably know it.) Then write your own nursery rhyme, using this pattern.

Hickory, dickory, dock,

The mouse ran up the clock;

The clock struck one,

The mouse ran down,

Hickory, dickory, dock.

110

New Rhyme for Hickory Dickory Dock

Try one of these lines to get started:

Hickory, dickory, dog / Lickety, rickety, run

We hope you had fun writing in your Buddy Book. Keep writing!

— Your Book Buddies